IS IT PASSOVER YET?

CHRIS BARASH

Pictures by
**ALESSANDRA
PSACHAROPULO**

SCHOLASTIC INC.

When spring flowers bloom
and grass starts to grow

And the warm sun has melted
that old winter snow...

Passover is on its way.

When we see from the
window a robin or wren

And squirrels play high up in the trees once again...

Passover is on its way.

When everyone scurries
from room to room

With a bucket and mop or a long-handled broom...

Passover is on its way.

When all of the windows and floors start to shine

And our whole house smells clean and looks extra fine...

Passover is on its way.

When our fanciest dishes come out of the drawer
And Elijah's cup sparkles like diamonds galore...

Passover is on its way.

When our house smells of kugel and sweet matzo cake
And cinnamon for the charoset we'll make...

Passover is on its way.

When the sun's getting low and the doorbell stops ringing

And everyone's ready for stories and singing...

When the Seder is ready and candles are lit

And Nana's shown everyone just where to sit...

Passover is here!

ISBN 978-1-338-03622-0

12 11 10 9 8 7 6 5 4 3 2 1   16 17 18 19 20 21

Printed in the U.S.A.   40

First Scholastic printing, March 2016

Design by Jordan Kost